Luna Peak Publishing, Sierra Madre, California.
www.lunapeakpublishing.com

ISBN: 978-1-7355958-4-9
Printed and bound in the United States of America.
Cover art and design by Yolandi Oosthuizen.

The Grief Workbook

Grief Tested, Mourner Approved!

By Gracelyn Bateman & Melody Lomboy-Lowe

Honestly,

grief is quite terrible. Since we're in it for the long haul,

we might as well have some fun as we work through it.

This workbook is inspired by our personal grief experiences,

and this is a new way to engage with grief through humor,

games and prompts. Everyone grieves differently, and with that

in mind, hopefully you'll find pages in here that will help you

reflect on your grief and remember your loved ones.

Take your time. Remember, you are not

alone in your grief.

- Gracelyn & Melody, your grief friends

This book belongs to:

Year:

Who You Are Grieving:

_____

_____

Their Relationship(s) to You:

_____

_____

Important Dates in Your Grief:

_____

_____

Blank pages can be used for further reflection,
or to duplicate your answers for other losses.

Loss-Word Puzzle

Solve the crossword puzzle of common (and sometimes cringey) condolences.

DOWN

1. "Stay _____ for your family"

4. "They would want you to be _____"

5. "Let me know if I can do anything to ____"

6. "Everything happens for a _____"

8. "Isn't it time to ____ on?"

ACROSS

2. "You're going to be __"

3. "_____ and prayers"

7. "They're in a better _____"

9. "I'm _____ for your loss"

10. "Heaven gained another _____"

What was something said as a condolence for
your loss? How did you react?

_____

_____

_____

_____

_____

_____

_____

_____

_____

Top Tear (Tier) Grief

Color in each level of grief-crying that you
have unlocked. Remember, it is normal and healthy
to cry and let it out!

Cried while walking down the street

Cried at the convenience store

Cried in class or in a meeting

Cried at a sit-down restaurant

Cried at the grocery store

Cried in the shower

Cried in the car

Share about a place where you have cried
or grieved in public.

_____

_____

_____

_____

_____

_____

_____

_____

_____

_____

Grief Mythbusters

Before I experienced grief, I thought it would feel like:

Now that I have experienced grief, it feels like:

SHOCKING!

What has shocked you about your grief
process so far?

_____

_____

_____

_____

_____

_____

_____

_____

_____

_____

_____

Would You Rather

··· PART 1 ···

What feels good for your grief?
Choose your preference.

Spend time outside	*or*	Spend time inside
Express emotions with others	*or*	Keep emotions private
Talk about your grief	*or*	Internalize your grief
Travel	*or*	Settle in
Share memories with others	*or*	Individual reflection
Be in the presence of others	*or*	Enjoy solo time

Are you surprised by any of your grief preferences?
Have your preferences changed over time?

_____

_____

_____

_____

_____

_____

_____

_____

_____

_____

_____

_____

Funeral Week

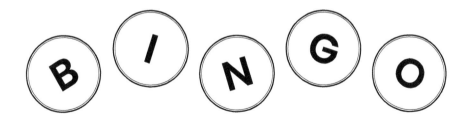

Was asked "how did they die?"	Feeling all eyes on you	Hid from relatives	Got a little obsessive when making the photo display	Ran out of tissues
Oops! Tried to call the person who died	Loud wailing from someone not close to the deceased	Gave the eulogy	Told a eulogy joke that didn't land	Heard a new, epic story about the deceased
Oh the funeral flowers die too? Everything is temporary	Asked "hey, how are you *really* doing though?"	FREE SAFE SPACE	Kind of surprised by the amount of ash	Ate everything in sight
Barely caught 1 full REM cycle all week	Surprised by the weight when pallbearing	Was told "you'll be OK" by a non-griever	Close friends didn't show up to the services	People came out of the woodwork to show up, it was awesome
Barely ate 1 full meal all week	Had trouble picking out your funeral outfit	Ruined your shoes in the wet cemetery grass	Blew a snot rocket during the service	Was told "you look great" at the service

What other bingo squares would you add?

Let's Talk About Them

Their Favorite

Color: _____

Nickname: _____

Food: _____

Drink: _____

Dessert: _____

Activity: _____

Plant or flower: _____

Movie or show: _____

Team: _____

Place: _____

Quote: _____

Hobby: _____

What were your favorite things to do together?

_____

_____

_____

_____

_____

_____

_____

_____

_____

_____

Your Supporters

Describe a recent act of kindness
from a supporter.

_____

_____

_____

_____

_____

Give a shout out to those who
have supported you.

_____

_____

_____

_____

_____

Anatomy of a Good Grief Supporter

Supporters show up with their whole selves!
Color in your friend.

Eyes
to observe your social cues and adjust their actions
and conversation accordingly

Ears
to actively listen
if you feel like sharing
memories or to hear
how you feel

Mouth
to remind you that you
won't go through this alone,
even if they don't know
what to say

Arms
to give you hugs for
comfort

Hands
to make you food and
deliver snacks

Legs
to take you on a walk for fresh air and vitamin D

What Is
One Thing...

... that you wish you knew sooner about grief?

Make your way through the maze
to find your grief community.

Start here!

End here!

Would You Rather

··· PART 2 ···

What feels good for your grief?
Choose your preference.

Keep old traditions	*or*	Create new traditions
Celebrate on birthdays and death anniversaries	*or*	Not celebrate on birthdays and death anniversaries
Listen to ambient sounds	*or*	Quiet reflection
Cope with dark humor	*or*	Keep it serious
Talk about them in the past tense	*or*	Talk about them in the present tense
Keep busy	*or*	Cut down obligations

What preferences do you feel are important for others in your life to know about?

_____

_____

_____

_____

_____

_____

_____

_____

_____

_____

Feeling Grief Physically

Circle where you physically feel your grief.

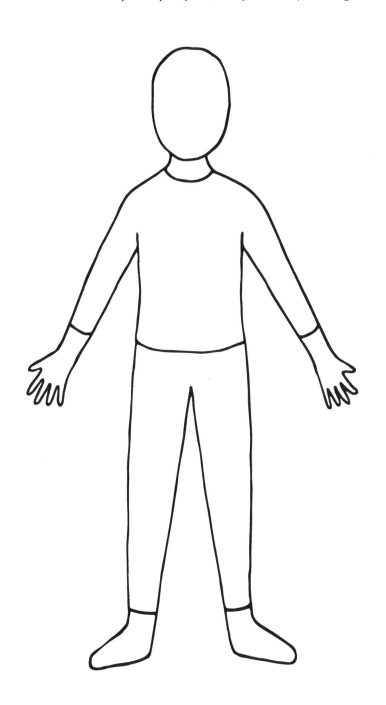

How does grief feel on your body?

_____

_____

_____

_____

_____

_____

_____

_____

_____

_____

Setting Boundaries

Society has not armed us with the right words to say to grievers, or the right ways for grievers to respond. Although people are generally well-intentioned, they may say or do unhelpful things. Let's map out some polite responses for setting boundaries. Color in the text bubbles below and add your own statements.

Has someone overstepped boundaries when trying to support your grief? What happened?

_____

_____

_____

_____

_____

_____

_____

_____

_____

_____

A Mixed Bag of Emotions

Grief can feel like a mixed bag of emotions. Circle some of the emotions you have felt during your grief so far.

Grief Feelings

What other feelings would you add to your
mixed bag of emotions?

_____

_____

_____

_____

_____

Have any of these emotions
surprised you?

_____

_____

_____

_____

_____

Have You Used the Grief Card?

OFFICIAL GRIEF CLUB MEMBER

Member Name:
....

Date Issued:
....

Valid Through: *Does not expire*
....

LUNA PEAK

RULES: This griever is exempt from specific activities, meetings, functions, and minor inconveniences. Griever may use this card at their discretion.

When and where have you used the grief card, or where would you like to use it?

_____

_____

_____

_____

_____

I'm "Lost for Words" Search

```
G E T R O F M O C K A S E M W
C O M M U N I T Y D U G G E T
S T U O M E H I E N D W T M N
Q O C O T E G R I E F W X O E
A J W E R I O S L I J J H R M
X C R A L N O W A R U F F I E
B Y P F O F O N H F Z X K E V
S Y Z H L N E P S O A Z Y S A
S Y H Y K E I R E C D Z X N E
M J V C U O P B T A G D Z M R
O W A U H X U I X J C S Z Z E
J K E S N X M X X J Z E Z J B
D O S B X Q P O K F W W K Y S
F S W L X N F Q B D I L H O Z
Y O T U S E O U S E P Q O Y R
```

Emotions   Grief   Reflect   Acknowledge

Comfort   Peace   Memories   Bereavement

Friend   Honor   Therapy   Community

On a Tough Grief Day

What do you like to eat?

What do you like to drink?

What are your favorite calming activities?

Who do you like to talk to, if you want to talk?

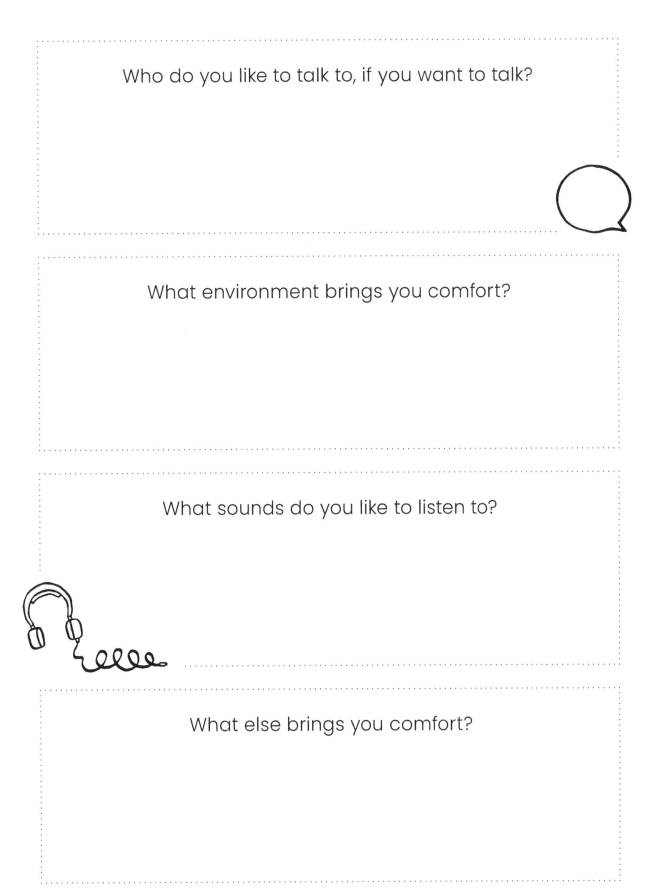

What environment brings you comfort?

What sounds do you like to listen to?

What else brings you comfort?

Collect Your Grief Gold Stars

Write out your accomplishments, big or small, on the badges below. We are proud of you for surviving grief!

What is one accomplishment post-loss that
you are particularly proud of?

_____

_____

_____

_____

_____

_____

_____

_____

_____

_____

Decorate the Tissue Box

Customize the tissue box with symbols of your grief.

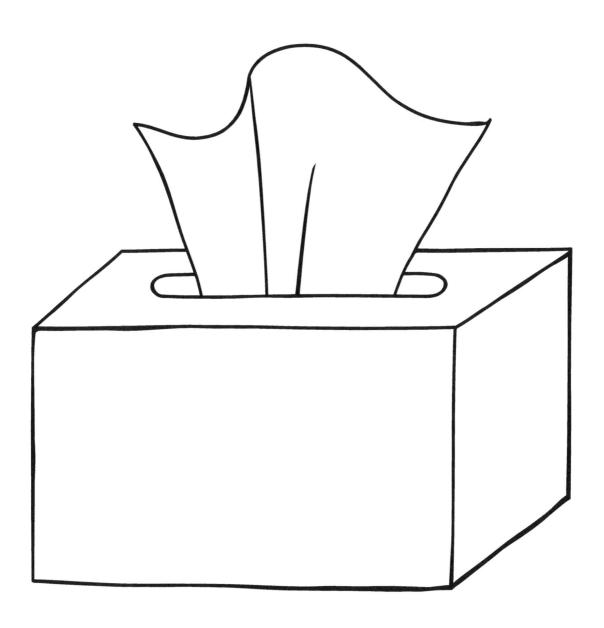

Why are these items symbolic to your grief?

_____

_____

_____

_____

_____

_____

_____

_____

_____

_____

THANK YOU!

What has been helpful for your grief?
Make a list of actions, things people have
said to you, etc.

PLEASE STOP!

What has been unhelpful for your grief?
Make a list of actions, things people have
said to you, etc.

_____

_____

_____

_____

_____

_____

_____

_____

_____

_____

Tune Into Your Grief

Let's make a grief playlist.

One song that
makes you smile:

_____

One new song
you think they would like:

_____

One classic
sad song:

_____

One song that
brings you joy:

_____

One song that
brings you to tears:

_____

One song that
makes you dance:

_____

One song that
you like to sing along to:

_____

Your favorite song to
play on a tough day:

_____

Has music or artistic expression played a role in your grief process? Share about it below.

_____

_____

_____

_____

_____

_____

_____

_____

_____

_____

Grief Comebacks

Here are some unfortunately common words said
to grievers, and ways for grievers to potentially respond.
Match up the assumptions on the left side with good grief
comebacks on the right side.

You're being negative.	My grief doesn't have a timeline. I want to talk about it.
It's been a long time. Why are you still talking about this?	Everyone grieves in different ways. Even if I don't bring it up, I still think about it often.
You talk about it too much.	Talking about it is helpful for me. My grief deserves to be honored and heard.
You never talk about it so I assumed you're fine.	Talking about grief is not being negative. I am experiencing something very difficult.

Has someone made an assumption about your grief? How did you respond, or how would you like to respond in the future?

_____

_____

_____

_____

_____

_____

_____

_____

_____

Grief is Like a Roller Coaster

List out the highs and lows of your grief experience so far.

Highs in your grief:

_____

_____

_____

Lows in your grief:

_____

_____

_____

How has your grief felt like a roller coaster?
What has thrown you for a loop?

_____

_____

_____

_____

_____

_____

_____

_____

_____

_____

Grief is Like...

What is grief like for you?
What would you compare it to?

_____

_____

_____

_____

_____

Draw out a metaphor for your grief.

Write Them a Letter

A memory that brings a smile to my face is...

A question I have for you is...

A memory that brings me comfort is...

Lately I've been feeling...

You wouldn't believe that...

I want you to know that...

Loss - Word Puzzle

Down:

1. Strong

4. Happy

5. Help

6. Reason

8. Move

Across:

2. OK

3. Thoughts

7. Place

9. Sorry

10. Angel

9 781735 595849